"WHAT DIFFERENCE DOES IT MAKE HOW MUCH YOU HAVE? WHAT YOU DO NOT HAVE AMOUNTS TO MUCH MORE."

— SENECA THE YOUNGER, ROMAN STOIC PHILOSOPHER (4 B.C. TO 65 A.D.)

NINE DAYS EARLIER, SIR RICHARD BRANSON, WORTH A MEASLY $4.4 BILLION, BEAT BEZOS INTO SPACE, LAUNCHING THE *V.S.S. UNITY*. WHY?

I'VE WANTED TO GO TO SPACE SINCE I WAS A KID, AND I WANT TO ENABLE HOPEFULLY HUNDREDS OF THOUSANDS OF OTHER PEOPLE OVER THE NEXT 100 YEARS TO BE ABLE TO GO TO SPACE.

NOW BOOKING FOR 2025, YOU, TOO, CAN FLY TO THE EDGE OF SPACE FOR $125,000 U.S.D. THE FIRST THIRTY FLIGHTS BY VIRGIN GALACTIC ARE SOLD OUT. SORRY.

"IF YOU WANT TO KNOW WHAT GOD THINKS ABOUT MONEY, JUST LOOK AT THE PEOPLE HE GIVES IT TO."

– DOROTHY PARKER, AMERICAN POET, 1893-1967 A.D.

"IT SEEMS LIKE THE MORE I GIVE, THE MORE I GET, AND THAT IS THE WAY IT IS SUPPOSED TO GO IN LIFE. MONEY IS LIKE THE TIDE; IT ROLLS IN, AND IT ROLLS OUT. IF YOU CLUTCH IT, YOU ARE NOT GOING TO KEEP IT."

"I GIVE BACK TO THE COMMUNITY BUT ALSO ENJOY PRIVILEGES. TO DO OTHERWISE WOULD BE AN INSULT TO GOD."

HER WILLINGNESS TO SHARE WHAT SHE HAS WITH THOSE LESS FORTUNATE COMES FROM HER UPBRINGING.

LOCUST RIDGE, ON THE BANKS OF THE LITTLE PIGEON RIVER, TENNESSEE: 1958

OKAY, YOUR TURN, DOLLY REBECCA.

IT'S TOO COLD, MAMA.

HUSH, CHILD, I'M WARMING IT UP. GET IN.

THE WATER'S ALL CLOUDY. I THINK MY SISTER WAS PRETTY DIRTY.

I WAS NOT! TAKE THAT BACK!

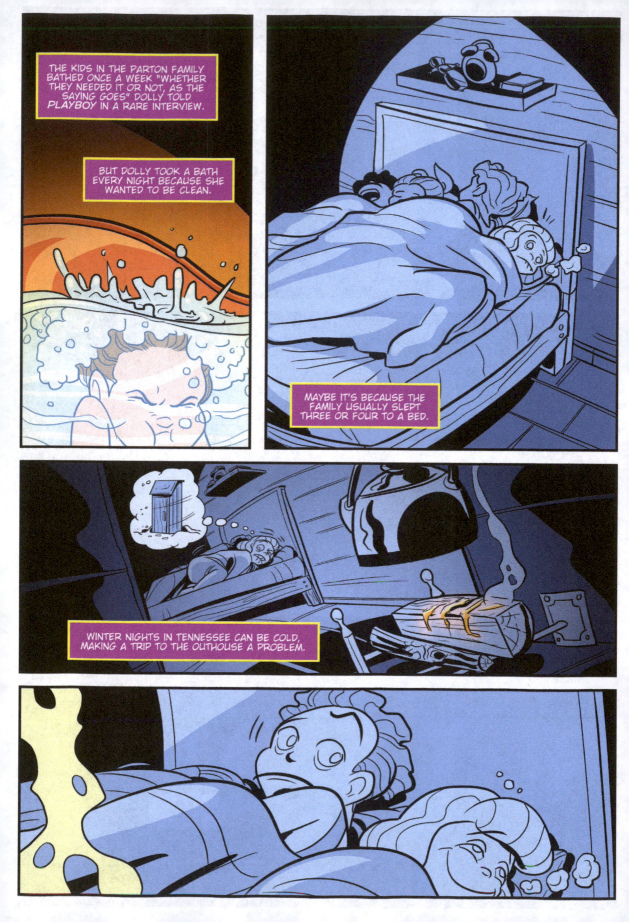

THE KIDS IN THE PARTON FAMILY BATHED ONCE A WEEK "WHETHER THEY NEEDED IT OR NOT, AS THE SAYING GOES" DOLLY TOLD *PLAYBOY* IN A RARE INTERVIEW.

BUT DOLLY TOOK A BATH EVERY NIGHT BECAUSE SHE WANTED TO BE CLEAN.

MAYBE IT'S BECAUSE THE FAMILY USUALLY SLEPT THREE OR FOUR TO A BED.

WINTER NIGHTS IN TENNESSEE CAN BE COLD, MAKING A TRIP TO THE OUTHOUSE A PROBLEM.

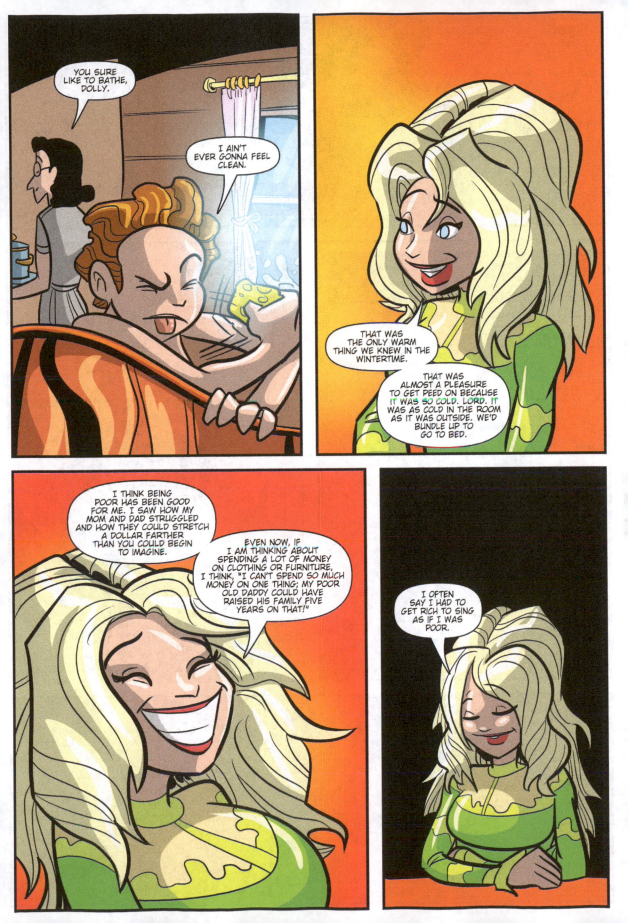

THE SHOW FEATURED A WHO'S WHO OF COUNTRY MUSIC ROYALTY, SUCH AS ROY ACUFF, CHET ATKINS, AND JIMMY MARTIN.

"IF YOUR ACTIONS CREATE A LEGACY THAT INSPIRES OTHERS TO DREAM MORE, LEARN MORE, DO MORE, AND BECOME MORE, THEN YOU ARE AN EXCELLENT LEADER," SHE TOLD AN INTERVIEWER.

DOLLY CAPTIVATED RADIO AUDIENCES WITH HER VOICE AND MATURITY THAT SEEMED TO BELIE HER YEARS.

"IT'S HARD TO BE A DIAMOND IN A RHINESTONE WORLD."

SINCE THE FAMILY DIDN'T HAVE A CAR, SHE RODE THE BUS TO THE STATION.

IN 1957, DOLLY AND HER UNCLE BILL WROTE "PUPPY LOVE" AND "GIRL LEFT ALONE."

THEY RECORDED THE SINGLE IN LAKE CHARLES, LOUISIANA, AT GOLDBAND RECORDS IN 1959.

IT WAS A 30-HOUR BUS RIDE FROM PIGEON FORGE.

"I DON'T THINK I'LL EVER FORGET THE WAY THE INSIDE OF THAT BUS SMELLED. IT WAS A COMBINATION OF DIESEL FUEL, NAUGAHYDE, AND PEOPLE WHO WERE GOING PLACES."

THE SINGLE DIDN'T SET THE CHARTS ON FIRE, BUT IT DID INSPIRE DOLLY TO WRITE MORE.

"DADDY RAISED THAT WHOLE FAMILY ON HIS BRAINS AND HARD WORK," PARTON WROTE IN HER 2020 BOOK, *SONGTELLER: MY LIFE IN LYRICS.*

HOWEVER, HE WAS ALWAYS "KIND OF ASHAMED" THAT HE NEVER LEARNED TO READ OR WRITE.

"HE WAS SUCH A SMART PERSON. I ALWAYS THOUGHT THAT IF DADDY HAD AN EDUCATION, THERE'S NO TELLING WHAT HE COULD HAVE BEEN."

HE GREW UP IN A FAMILY OF FIFTEEN KIDS, "BACK IN THE MOUNTAINS," AS DOLLY DESCRIBED HIS HOME.

THE ONE-ROOM SCHOOLHOUSE THAT SERVED HIS AREA WAS MILES AWAY, AND CHILDREN HAD TO WORK THE FIELDS TO FEED THE FAMILY.

WEATHER, HARVEST SEASON, HUNTING SEASON, AND MORE AFFECTED HOW AND WHEN KIDS ATTENDED SCHOOL. SOMETIMES, THE HASSLE SIMPLY WASN'T WORTH IT.

"HE KNEW EXACTLY WHAT EVERYTHING WAS WORTH, HOW MUCH HE WAS GOING TO MAKE FROM THAT TOBACCO CROP, WHAT HE COULD TRADE, AND HOW HE COULD MAKE IT ALL WORK."

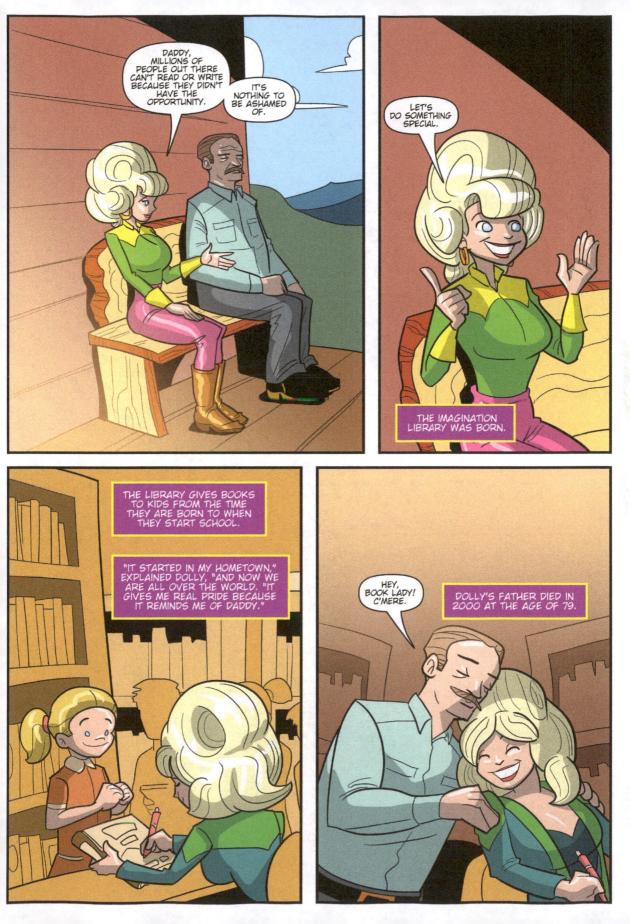

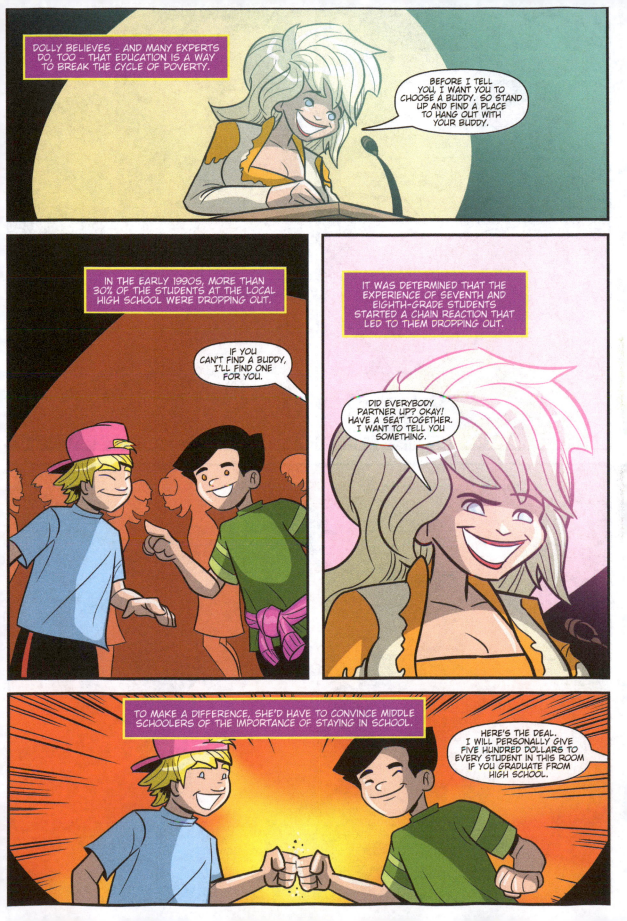

DOLLY? WHAT ABOUT YOU?

IF ALL ADULTS COMPLETED HIGH SCHOOL OR A SECONDARY-SCHOOL EQUIVALENT, GLOBAL POVERTY COULD BE CUT IN HALF.

I'M GOING TO NASHVILLE TO BE A STAR.

HAHAHAHAHA!

"I DIDN'T KNOW WHAT WAS AWAITING ME," DOLLY WROTE IN HER BOOK. "I DIDN'T KNOW WHAT I WAS GOING TO DO. BUT I KNEW I DIDN'T HAVE TO WORRY ABOUT BEING POOR.

THANKS FOR THE SUPPORT, YA'LL.

"I KNEW THAT I COULD ALWAYS COME BACK HOME. SO I TOLD MY FOLKS THAT I WASN'T GOING TO UNTIL I HAD SOMETHING TO SHOW FOR IT."

TIDALWAVE
COMICS

Michael Frizell — Writer

Ramon Salas — Art

Benjamin Glibert — Letters

Darren G. Davis — Editor

Ramon Salas — Cover

Cover B: Joe Phillips
Cover C: Joe Paradise

Darren G. Davis
Publisher

Maggie Jessup
Publicity

Susan Ferris
Entertainment Manager

TIDALWAVE
PRODUCTIONS

CPSIA information can be obtained
at www.ICGtesting.com
Printed in the USA
LVHW061830191022
731081LV00002B/29